GROSS SCIENCE EXPERIMENTS

FOR KIDS

25+ Fun and Challenging **Experiments** for Boys and Girls **STEM** **AGE 6-12** YEARS OLD

TIP FOR PARENTS:

Parents, talk with your kids before each experiment and teach them along the way how science is a part of things we do everyday. For example, when cooking, the slightest deviation in recipes can result in disaster!

PARENTAL SUPERVISION IS ALWAYS RECOMMENDED

DO NOT EAT any of the experiments.

If ingested, seek medical help immediately.

Wash your hands before and after each experiment.

Not recommended for ages 5 & under.

CHOKING HAZARD - MAY CONTAIN SMALL PARTS

Your Crazy Uncle is NOT responsible for any accidents or damage that may occur.

GROSS SCIENCE EXPERIMENTS FOR KIDS

This Gross Science Book Belongs to: _____

GROSS SCIENCE EXPERIMENTS FOR KIDS

Enter at your own risk, gross science is not for the faint of heart!
Before you start this book, let's talk about the rules.

RULE #1

Some experiments will require parental supervision, and others should only be conducted outside. If this is the case, you will see one of the above warning signs.

RULE #2

Read the instructions ALL the way through before beginning any experiment, and make sure you have permission from your parents.

RULE #3

Read the instructions ALL the way through before beginning any experiment, and make sure you have permission from your parents.

EDIBLE SNOT

INGREDIENTS

- 2/3 cup corn syrup
- 1 cup sugar
- 1/2 cup water
- 1 tablespoon butter
- 1 tablespoon cornstarch
- Pinch of salt

ADULT HELP REQUIRED

- Food coloring (yellow or green)
- Candy thermometer

INSTRUCTIONS

Bring all of your ingredients, besides the food coloring, to a boil in a medium sized saucepan. As the saucepan is heating up, stir the ingredients together so they combine. Once the candy is boiling, do not stir any longer. Put the candy thermometer in the mixture and once the temperature hits 250°F remove it from the heat immediately. Add in your food coloring and pour your mixture onto a butter plate. Let cool for 20 minutes. Once the taffy is cool, butter your fingers and start pulling it apart. It won't be as hard as traditional taffy, but doesn't it look like snot? How cool is that?!

THE SCIENCE BEHIND IT

Heating up sugar to a certain degree will make it harden as it cools. The higher the temperature goes, the harder your candy will be!

CHALLENGE

Can you convince someone that the slime you made is real snot?!

MOLDY BREAD

INGREDIENTS

- Bread
- Multiple paper and plastic bags
- Paper Plate
- Permanent marker
- Water

INSTRUCTIONS

We are going to see in what environments bread molds quickest. We will test bread in different types of bags in different lights. First, you'll need to divide the bread into six pieces. Very slightly add moisture to the pieces of bread. Place two pieces in plastic bags, two in paper bags, and two on separate paper plates. Now place one of each in the light, and one of each in the dark. Now, we wait. It could take a few days for the mold to show up, so be patient!

THE SCIENCE BEHIND IT

Mold needs water, food, and oxygen to grow. Each piece of bread will have even amounts of food and water, but different amounts of oxygen. Which do you think will grow the most mold?

CHALLENGE

Write down which piece of bread you think will mold first!

NAKED EGGS

INGREDIENTS

- Eggs
- White vinegar
- Clear jar

INSTRUCTIONS

Fill the jar with white vinegar and place the eggs inside the jar. In about 15 minutes, you'll see bubbles forming around the egg. You'll need to wait about 8 hours to see the eggs start spinning as the gasses release from the egg. It looks like they're dancing doesn't it?! The egg will start to crack and absorb the liquid and release some of its shell. After about 3 days, you'll have a completely naked egg!

THE SCIENCE BEHIND IT

Egg shells are made of Calcium. When you put the egg in vinegar (an acid), it begins to break down the calcium. Eventually, the calcium will completely disintegrate.

CHALLENGE

Once you have your naked egg, try to play an egg toss! How long do you think it will take to burst?!

UNPOPPABLE BUBBLE

INGREDIENTS

- Pipettes, or bubble sticks
- Cotton gloves
- 2 cups Water
- Scissors
- 1/4 cup Dish soap
- 2 Tbsps. Glycerin (Found at craft stores)

INSTRUCTIONS

Combine the wet ingredients and stir together. Put on your cotton gloves before blowing the bubbles, they provide a soft place for the bubbles to land! Next, cut the thick end of your pipette or grab a spare bubble stick and dip the end into the mixture and blow your bubbles like you know how!

THE SCIENCE BEHIND IT

Adding glycerin to your bubble mixture, makes the soap layers thicker, as well as allowing for the water in the soap to evaporate much less quickly. This makes your bubbles stronger!

CHALLENGE

Can you blow several bubbles and stack them on top of each other?

PLASTIC MILK

- Bowl
- 1 cup Milk
- 3 Tbsps. Vinegar
- Strainer
- Food coloring (optional)

INSTRUCTIONS

Warm up the milk in the microwave, about a minute and a half. Next, mix in the vinegar. Stir for about one minute as the milk clumps up. Strain the milk through a strainer and push the clumps against the metal to get all the water out. Finally, dump the clumps on a paper towel to get the remaining water out. You can now color or mold your plastic if you'd like. If you do mold it into a shape, let it dry for two days to cure!

THE SCIENCE BEHIND IT

Vinegar is an acid, and when you mix it in milk it breaks down the protein in the liquid.

CHALLENGE

What can you make with your plastic? Try to form a heart or a star!

BURPING BAGGIES

INGREDIENTS

- Quart-sized Ziploc bags
- 1/3 cup Vinegar
- 2 Tbsps. Baking soda
- 1/4 cup Water
- 1-ply paper towel (you can separate a 2-ply paper towel)

- Food coloring
- Glitter or sprinkles

INSTRUCTIONS

Wrap the baking soda into the paper towel. Mix the vinegar and warm water together (not in the pouch yet). Place your food coloring and glitter or sprinkles in the pouch. Now, pour the vinegar mixture into the baggie. Carefully, place the wrapped baking soda into the baggie without getting the baking soda wet. Make sure the ziploc is securely zipped. Now shake it a little bit and set it on the ground!

THE SCIENCE BEHIND IT

When vinegar and baking soda are combined, carbon dioxide (a type of air) is created! That's why your baggie got so full, it was airing up from the inside!

CHALLENGE

Grab a friend and see who can make their bag burp the loudest!

QUICKSAND CATASTROPHE

INGREDIENTS

- 1 cup Water
- 1-2 cups Cornstarch
- Mixing bowl
- Food coloring (Optional)

INSTRUCTIONS

To begin, pour one cup of cornstarch into a large bowl, and notice how smooth the powder is. Add your food coloring to the water, then pour it over the cornstarch and start mixing it with your hands as you go. Keep adding water until the mixture becomes hard when you tap it. If it's too runny, add more cornstarch. Now, prepare to get messy! Notice that now that your quicksand is complete, if you grab it in your hand then it gets hard, but if you open your palm then it runs like liquid! Do you see why quicksand is so hard to get out of now?!

THE SCIENCE BEHIND IT

The cornstarch-and-water mixture creates a fluid that acts more like quicksand than water: applying force (squeezing or tapping it) causes it to become thicker.

CHALLENGE

If you were trapped in a tub of quicksand, what would be the best way to escape?

GERM MADNESS

INGREDIENTS

- Hand lotion
- Glitter
- Sink
- Paper towels
- Soap
- Water

ADULT HELP REQUIRED

INSTRUCTIONS

Get a dab of lotion and evenly rub it in your hands. Have your adult helper get a pinch of glitter and put it in the palm of your hand. Invision the glitter as germs. Now, put your hand in a fist and notice how the germs spread. Now touch your other palm, shake someone's hand, grab a bottle of water. Do you see where the germs went? Now try to wipe off your hand with a paper towel. Did it help? Now wash with just water, did it help? Finally, wash your hands with soap and water. Did the germs finally come off? Washing your hands is so important because germs spread so quickly.

THE SCIENCE BEHIND IT

Germs are much smaller than what the human eye can see, so this experiment helps put into perspective just how small and quickly they spread! Remember, washing your hands with water AND soap is always the best way to get rid of them.

CHALLENGE

Show a friend this experiment and see the look of surprise on their face!

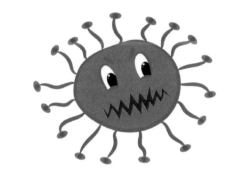

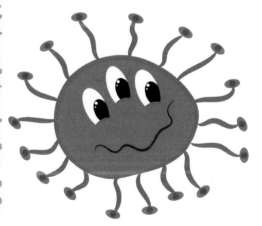

ELEPHANT SOAP

INGREDIENTS

- Ivory soap bar
- Microwaveable Plate
- Microwave

INSTRUCTIONS

Place your ivory soap on a microwaveable plate. Microwave the soap for 2 minutes. Watch the soap grow as it microwaves. By the end of the 2 minutes, you'll have a large cloud of soap!

THE SCIENCE BEHIND IT

Did you know Ivory soap is the only brand of soap that floats in water? Why do you think that is? There are tiny air pockets containing water molecules whipped into the soap as it's being made. When you heat up those molecules, the air pockets expand creating your soap cloud!

CHALLENGE

With a friend, microwave a bar of soap each. At the end of the 2 minutes, who has the largest soap cloud?

GROWING MOLD

- Unflavored gelatin
- Q-tips
- 6 Sanitized mason jars

ADULT HELP REQUIRED

INSTRUCTIONS

Make the gelatin first. Boil 2 cups of water and prepare the gelatin according to the package instructions. Stir the gelatin until it dissolves, then divide it into your containers. Be sure to seal your jars so no dust gets in them before we start the experiment. Let the gelatin solidify for a few hours. Now, get your q-tips and wet them. Go around your house and decide which areas you think are the dirtiest. Some ideas are the stove, toilet, front doorknob, shower floor, or your hands. After you've swabbed the areas, rub the q-tip all over the gelatin (be careful to not rip up the gelatin) in the jar and label which area it was swabbed from. Try to guess which area will make the most mold grow, and be sure to write down your guesses! Place your jars in a dark room. After 24 hours, you will have mold growing, but give it a week and see how large it gets! Who guessed correctly?!

THE SCIENCE BEHIND IT

Mold needs water, food, and oxygen to grow. Whichever area has the most of these components should grow the most mold!

CHALLENGE

Write down which areas of the house you think will produce the most mold!

ICE CREAM IN A BAG

INGREDIENTS

- Cream
- Ziploc
- Salt

INSTRUCTIONS

Start by pouring your cream into a Ziploc bag, and add salt. Prior to sealing it closed, make sure all the air is completely out of the bag. Now time for the fun, shake your bag vigorously for about 7-10 minutes. After you're done shaking, notice how the cream has transformed into ice cream! Grab a spoon and enjoy it!

THE SCIENCE BEHIND IT

Adding salt to the cream lowers its freezing point. The salt lowers the temperature around the cream, resulting in homemade ice cream!

CHALLENGE

Make several bags of your mixture. Shake one slowly for 10 minutes, and shake the other quickly for 10 minutes. Does the speed of shaking change how the cream comes together?

MAGNETIC SLIME

INGREDIENTS

- 1 1/2 Tbsps. Liquid Starch
- 1/4 cup Elmer's glue
- 2 Tbsps. Iron Oxide powder

- Bowl
- Plastic spoons
- Magnet

INSTRUCTIONS

Pour 1/4 cup Elmer's glue and 2 tablespoons of iron oxide powder into your bowl and stir together. Next, pour in 1.5 tablespoons of the liquid starch and stir together until your slime forms. Knead the slime together with your hands! If your slime is too sticky, knead in a little more starch. If it's too loose, knead in more glue. Now, grab your magnet and play with your slime! See if you can move it from one side of the table without touching the slime! Be careful- magnets are very strong! Keep them away from your electronic devices.

THE SCIENCE BEHIND IT

Iron is a metal, and magnets attract metal objects. The slime adheres to the different iron particles, meaning it holds onto them tight enough that it won't let go.

CHALLENGE

See who can create the tallest slime mountain without ever touching your slime!

SCIENCE BALLOON

INGREDIENTS

- Baking soda
- Vinegar
- Empty water bottle
- Balloon

INSTRUCTIONS

Pour the vinegar into a water bottle, about halfway up. Then, pour a few tablespoons of baking soda into the balloon. To complete this experiment, connect the unblown balloon to the top of the water bottle (opened), and lift the balloon vertically. The chemical reaction when the baking soda falls in the vinegar will begin blowing up your balloon!

THE SCIENCE BEHIND IT

When you mix baking soda and vinegar, they create what is called a chemical reaction. This reaction releases carbon dioxide, which fills the balloon.

CHALLENGE

Who can fill their balloon the fastest? Who's balloon can travel the highest!

SNOTTY RAINFALL

INGREDIENTS

- Jar
- Water
- Shaving cream
- Green food coloring

INSTRUCTIONS

To begin, fill your empty jar with water about 3/4 of the way. Add a layer of shaving cream directly on top of the water. Lastly, drop a few drops of the green food coloring on top and wait for the rain to fall! Place your jar down on a flat surface and take a look, pretty cool!

THE SCIENCE BEHIND IT

As water begins to mix with the shaving cream, the shaving cream gets heavier and heavier. Eventually, it will get so heavy that it starts to fall. The green food coloring helps the shaving cream cloud look like snot!

CHALLENGE

Who's snotty rain will fall first? Who will have the most rain fall at one time?

HURRICANE IN A BOTTLE

INGREDIENTS

- Jar with lid
- Water
- 1 Tsp. Dish soap
- Food coloring (Color of your choice)

INSTRUCTIONS

Grab your jar and fill it up to be about 3/4 full of water. In a separate small bowl, mix together the dish soap and a few drops of food coloring. Once it is mixed well, pour the mixture into the jar of water and secure the lid. Now, shake the jar vigorously and water the storm break out!

THE SCIENCE BEHIND IT

When you swirl the water, it rotates in the direction you swirl it. The different pressures at the top of the bottle where there's air and the bottom of the bottle cause a cyclone to form. The heavy pressure at the bottom pulls the lighter pressure at the top down.

CHALLENGE

Challenge a friend and see who can make their hurricane last the longest!

SNOT COLORED FLOWERS

INGREDIENTS

- 3 Cups
- Carnations
- Food coloring (Green and Yellow)
- Water

INSTRUCTIONS

Start by pouring water into each cup, about 3/4 full. Add 13-15 drops of food coloring into each cup. Carefully, cut the bottom of the stems on each carnation and place a few of them into each cup. Water the colors defy gravity and make their way to the flower petals, causing them to change colors! Viola, you have yellow and green flowers now!

THE SCIENCE BEHIND IT

The veins in the flower stems act as tunnels, transporting much needed nutrients to the flower. In this case, the veins soak in the water, and the food coloring stains the stem as it travels.

CHALLENGE

See what different color combinations you can make with your flowers!

WHY WE BRUSH OUR TEETH

INGREDIENTS

- 4 Cups
- Water
- Gatorade
- Permanent marker
- Fruit juice
- Soda
- 4 Eggs

INSTRUCTIONS

Start by telling your child that our teeth and eggs are both made up of calcium. When we drink sugary drinks, it breaks down the calcium or stains our teeth! Pour the liquids into 4 cups, one for each liquid. Label each cup with what drink is inside of it. Place an egg in each drink. Wait 24 hours and see what the drinks did to the egg. Notice how the colored fruit juice caused stains on the egg, while soda makes the egg feel soft and weak.

THE SCIENCE BEHIND IT

The sugar in each drink breaks down the calcium in the egg shell. The tannins (color) in the fruit juice cause stains.

CHALLENGE

Cover one egg with toothpaste and leave one uncovered. Place both in a cup with soda. See how the toothpaste protects the eggshell!

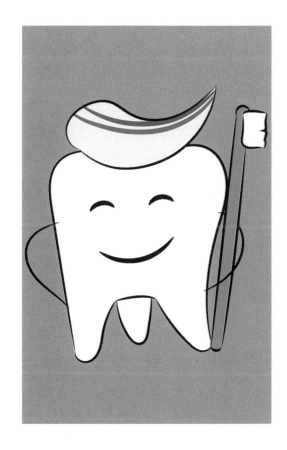

GERMY MARBLE PAINTING

INGREDIENTS

- Water
- Green food coloring
- Oil

- Heavy paper
- Dropper
- Baking dish

INSTRUCTIONS

To begin, mix the water and food coloring together and pour it into a baking dish. Place the piece of paper into the mixture so it is completely submerged. Now, pour a small amount of oil into a cup and add it into your dropper. Time for the fun, add a few drops of oil on top of your paper and watch the marble effect!

Tip: Don't add too much oil or the paper won't pick up the coloring. Start slow and only do a drop at a time.

THE SCIENCE BEHIND IT

Oil is less dense than water, meaning they cannot mix together. When you drop the green water on the paper, it cannot mix with the oil on the paper.

CHALLENGE

Draw shapes on your paper with the oil, then drop the green water on the rest of the paper. See how the shapes appear!

BUILD YOUR OWN EARWAX

INGREDIENTS

- 4 cups Vinegar
- 4 Tbsps. Baking soda
- Cooking pot
- Green food coloring
- Glass jar
- Paper plate

INSTRUCTIONS

Pour your vinegar into a pot and slowly add in baking soda, the solution will fizz so take your time mixing it! Add some green food coloring to the mixture. Bring your ingredients to a boil for over an hour and reduce to about a cup of liquid. You should see crystals forming around the edges of your pot. If you don't, keep boiling it until 3/4 cup. Put your new solution in a glass jar and let cool in the refrigerator for about 45 mins. Keep some of your crystals from the pan and place on a plate, they will be used as your "seed" for the earwax. Once your solution is cooled, you can pour it over the crystals. It should grow upwards and look like a tower of earwax!

THE SCIENCE BEHIND IT

When mixed and boiled, the ingredients make a solution called "sodium acetate". When you pour the sodium acetate on the leftover crystals, the crystals make the liquid sodium acetate turn into a solid.

CHALLENGE

Grab a friend and see who can grow their earwax the tallest!

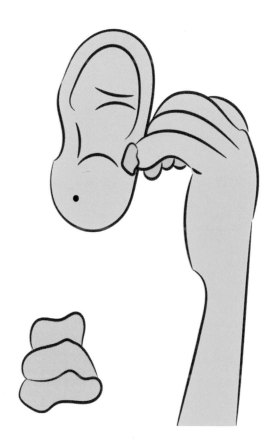

VANISHING COLORS

INGREDIENTS

ADULT HELP REQUIRED

- 3 Clear Plastic cups
- Water
- Yellow food coloring
- Bleach
- Pipette

INSTRUCTIONS

First, pour water into each clear plastic cup, about 3/4 of the way. Add a drop of food coloring to each cup and allow the colors to disperse into the water. Carefully, and with an adult's help, start adding a pipette full of bleach into each of the cups. Keep adding an additional pipette full of bleach until all the yellow is gone!

THE SCIENCE BEHIND IT

The bleach breaks apart the chemical bonds of color, changing the molecules so that there's no color left!

CHALLENGE

What happens when you try to add color back into the water and bleach solution?

ARTIC ANIMALS

INGREDIENTS

- Ice cubes
- Cold water
- Shortening
- Ziploc bags
- Bowl

INSTRUCTIONS

Place your bowl of water in the freezer to let it get very cold. Take it out and add in ice cubes. Place hands in the water to see how cold it is! Now, place shortening into a baggie and put your hand in the shortening. After your hand is covered in the shortening, place it in the cold water again. Did your hand get cold while it was in the water?

THE SCIENCE BEHIND IT

The shortening acts as a fatty, protective layer and absorbs the chilly temperature!

CHALLENGE

How long does it take your hand to feel the cold once it's wrapped in the protective shortening layer?

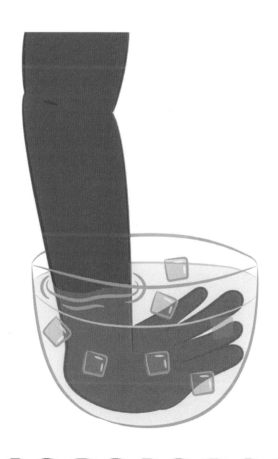

EXPLODING SODA

INGREDIENTS

- 2 liter Soda
- Mint Mentos
- Towels (For clean up)

OUTSIDE ONLY

INSTRUCTIONS

This is an outside activity, so bring your soda and mentos outside first! Next, unscrew your liter of soda and quickly add in 2 mentos. Step back and enjoy the show! Don't forget to clean up after!

THE SCIENCE BEHIND IT

The sodium bicarbonate in the mentos reacts with the acidity of the soda. Together, they cause a carbon dioxide explosion!

CHALLENGE

How huge can you make your explosion if you add double the amount of mentos?

WALKING ON EGGS

INGREDIENTS

- Two dozen eggs
- Towels (For clean up)

INSTRUCTIONS

Grab the whole family for this experiment! To begin, place the eggs in a line on the floor and ask everyone involved to remove their shoes and socks. One at a time, have each person walk across the eggs while being light on their heels and placing the egg into the arch of the foot. Did they break?!

THE SCIENCE BEHIND IT

The 3-dimensional arch is one of nature's strongest architectural forms - and that happens to be the shape of an egg! The arch allows pressure to be distributed evenly, and they become very strong.

CHALLENGE

How fast can you walk before an egg breaks?

POOP LAVA LAMP

INGREDIENTS

- Oil
- Brown paint
- Water Bottle
- Alka-seltzer tablet
- Clear cup

ADULT HELP REQUIRED

INSTRUCTIONS

Fill a clear cup with oil about 3/4 full. Mix some water and brown paint in a bowl and pour into the oil. Add some brown glitter and let everything settle in the bottom of the cup. Drop the Alka-seltzer tablet into the cup and watch your poop lava erupt!

THE SCIENCE BEHIND IT

Water and oil don't mix, but water and Alka-seltzer do! The Alka-seltzer reacts with the water, releasing carbon dioxide bubbles. Because the bubbles contain water, they don't mix with the oil but instead float to the top until the carbon dioxide starts losing its steam, causing it to float back down to the bottom.

CHALLENGE

How many poop lava bubbles do you think you can make before the carbon dioxide fizzes out?

WATER ABSORBS HEAT

INGREDIENTS

- 2 Balloons
- Candle
- Water

ADULT HELP REQUIRED

INSTRUCTIONS

Blow up one of your balloons and place it over a lit candle. How long did it take for the balloon to pop? Now fill your second balloon halfway with water, and blow up the other half. Now place that balloon over the same candle. Did it pop?!

THE SCIENCE BEHIND IT

Water absorbs heat because in order to increase its temperature, the water molecules must move faster. When the molecules move faster, they break up, and absorb the heat.

CHALLENGE

Fill balloons up with different amounts of water and see how long it takes each of them to pop!

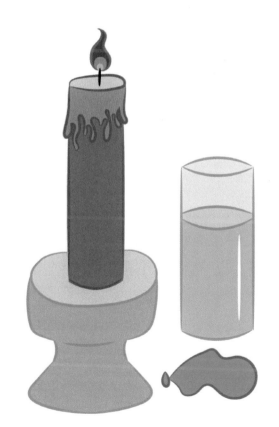

MOLDY PENNIES

INGREDIENTS

- Bowl
- Paper towel
- Pennies
- Vinegar

INSTRUCTIONS

Put your paper towel in a bowl and place your pennies on top. Pour vinegar over the pennies and leave them to sit overnight. After waiting over night, go see your moldy pennies!

THE SCIENCE BEHIND IT

The acid in the vinegar reacts with the moldy layer of copper oxide on the pennies. The copper oxide breaks up and makes the pennies shiny again.

CHALLENGE

Repeat the steps multiple times to see how shiny your pennies become!

EXPLODING SNOT

INGREDIENTS

- 1 Tbsp. Baking Soda (rounded)
- 1/3 cup Vinegar
- Green food coloring
- Tape
- Single ply paper towel
- Ziploc bag
- Pan

INSTRUCTIONS

Wrap one tablespoon of baking soda into a single ply paper towel. Use a piece of tape to secure it shut. Grab your baggie, and pour 1/3 cup of vinegar into the bag and add some green food coloring. This next action must be done quickly. You'll need one person to drop in the baking soda wrap. You'll need another to hold open the baggie, and secure it shut very quickly. Once the Baking soda is in the baggie, secure it shut very quickly. Once shut, shake the bag three times then place in a pan and step back! Don't forget to clean up your "snot"!

THE SCIENCE BEHIND IT

The baking soda and vinegar react, forming carbon dioxide. When closed in the baggie, the carbon dioxide has nowhere to go. The carbon dioxide will keep expanding, causing the explosion!

CHALLENGE

See who can create the biggest explosion!

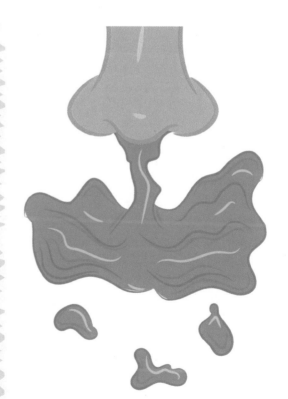

BOOGER LENSES

INGREDIENTS

- 1 Pkg. Jello
- Green food coloring
- 3/4 cup Water
- Measuring spoons/cups
- Paper towels
- Cutting board

ADULT HELP REQUIRED

INSTRUCTIONS

Start by heating the 3/4 cup of water in the microwave for a minute and a half. Pour the gelatin in the bowl with the food coloring and hot water and mix until combined. Let the liquid cool for 10 minutes. Cover a cutting board with some paper towels. Fill your measuring cups and measuring spoons with the mixture, and place them on the covered cutting board. Be careful not to spill, this is a sticky mess to clean up! Carefully move your cups and spoons into the fridge to cool and set for four hours. After four hours, remove your gelatin from the fridge and peel out your lenses from the spoons and cups.

TIP: Wet your fingers before you try to pull out the gelatin, it will keep it from sticking to your hands! Add a little water to a glass plate, then place one of your rounded lenses on the glass. Move it around to use it as a magnifying glass!

THE SCIENCE BEHIND IT

Light is bent as it moves through a lens. In this case, the jello acts as the lens!

CHALLENGE

Create a list of words to "hunt" for in a magazine or newspaper. Use your jello lens to find each word. The first person to find all their words is the winner!

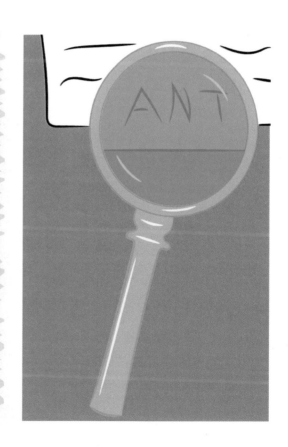

ELEPHANT TOOTHPASTE

INGREDIENTS

ADULT HELP REQUIRED

- 1/2 cup Hydrogen peroxide (6%)
- 1 Tsp. Yeast
- 2 Tbsp. Hot water
- Food coloring
- Dish soap
- Empty soda/water bottle (small)
- Tray
- Funnel (optional)

INSTRUCTIONS

Pour the hydrogen peroxide into the bottle. Mix the yeast into the water. Add the dish soap and food coloring to the hydrogen peroxide in the bottle. Add the yeast mixture to the bottle. Stand back and watch the reaction.

THE SCIENCE BEHIND IT

The yeast in this experiment acts as a catalyst, meaning it speeds up reactions. The hydrogen peroxide is broken down, releasing tiny oxygen bubbles. The oxygen bubbles attach to the other ingredients, making some pretty awesome foam!

CHALLENGE

Who's foam can form the fastest? The warmest? The highest?

WATCH WATER WALK

INGREDIENTS

- 3 Clear cups
- Water
- Blue food coloring
- Paper towels

INSTRUCTIONS

Fill two cups with water and stir blue food coloring into one cup, and yellow into the other. Place the third cup in between the two cups and fold two paper towels horizontally three times. Place one end of each paper towel in the colored water, and the other end in the empty cup. Watch the water move from one cup to the other. Does it make a new color? Try this out with several colors and see what colors you can make!

THE SCIENCE BEHIND IT

Water molecules stick to each other AND to the paper towel fibers. The paper towel fibers are more adhesive than the cohesive forces of water. The water is able to cling to the paper towel fibers and "walk" from cup to cup!

CHALLENGE

See what color combinations you can come up with!

CHECK OUT OUR NEXT BOOK!

P IS FOR POOP

A LAUGH-OUT-LOUD ACTIVITY BOOK FOR KIDS

WORD SCRAMBLES, COLORING PAGES, MAZES AND
MORE ACTIVITY WORKBOOK FOR BOYS AND GIRLS
AGE 4-6

If you enjoyed this book, please
leave a 5-star review on Amazon!